Steam on the Road

'Steaming through the ages'. An early Dutch
steam locomotive with a haphazard steering
mechanism.

D. D. Gladwin

Steam On The Road

B. T. Batsford Ltd, London

ISBN 0 7134 5712 0

Typeset by
Lasertext Ltd., Stretford, Manchester.
and printed in Great Britain by
Butler and Tanner, Frome, Somerset
for the publishers
B. T. Batsford Ltd
4 Fitzhardinge Street
London W1H 0AH

Introduction

Steam transport on the road conjures up different images for different people. For some it may be of traffic jams as a steam roller ambles along at little above walking speed or the uncanny swiftness of a big Sentinel on pneumatics as the driver makes up time. It may be that the picture is of clouds of steam emitting from every nook and cranny of an engine's motion, or black smoke gushing from the chimney and blanketing everything within 50 metres in an oily, greasy, sooty, murk. For me a perfect engine should have little steam escaping, smell of warm oil, run silently except for the odd click and creak of metal and, above all, give the impression of immense untapped power, a seeming ability to move anything anywhere. Not that steam was always so quiet, for around my part of the docks every morning at 5 am, six days a week, there was a horrendous crash as a laden Foden dropped its 20 tonnes or so of scrap metal into the hold of a coaster and, as it went off empty, the lorry then crashed and jangled its way over the cobbles.

Also, I remember the noise of the local fairground as it started to pack up in the early hours of the morning. Obscenities, large lumps of iron being thrown about, and spanners slung with great force upon the nearest noisy item contributed to the noise, but loudest of all was the clanging resonance of the crane-fitted showman's traction engine. Too much time spent on polish outside and too little on mechanical care for this already outmoded machine, had led to ill-fitting gears and linkages. Then, too, the stoker was usually too drunk to keep the fire in from one day to the next and he would, of necessity, try to work her long before she was warmed through. He dreamed of diesel while his negligence made the old-time steam drivers turn around in their graves as fast as they had once rotated their high gear.

Steam on the road, however, encompassed many aspects of transport, some of which had to all intents and purposes disappeared long before many of us were born. Around the turn of the century steam trams were, if not commonplace, an accepted part of man's industrial cities. Birmingham, Bradford, Bristol, Edinburgh, Leeds, London, Stoke-on-Trent, Swansea and Wigan all entered the roll-call of Britain's wealth and required a modern transport system.

Steam motorcycling is another aspect of the world of motoring that has disappeared for ever, defeated by its own complexity.

In 1906 steam omnibuses came within a hair's breadth of being established when the London General Omnibus Company ordered one hundred vehicles from Clarksons, the leading manufacturer. Probably only a dozen had been delivered when the order was cancelled, and with the cancellation the financial and moral incentive to improve the breed disappeared completely. The last steam bus of any real practicality ceased to run in 1919.

Fire engines were another aspect of machinery that was quickly superseded by the internal combustion engine (although I think the idea of a boiler near a fire infinitely preferable to a tank full of petrol!).

Could steam return to the roads to any extent? Of course it could, although probably not in its present (preserved) form, but the circumstances would have to be pretty extraordinary for such an event to take place. No doubt the vehicles could be made and perhaps, assuming solid fuel was used, some form of powdered anthracite could be injected into the firebox by remote control, to make the fuel cleaner and to reduce labour. Without doubt, some more adventurous drivers could be persuaded to volunteer for training, for there is still something that attracts people to steam.

Finding the illustrations used in this book has been a great pleasure, which should be reflected in the choice offered, but a brief word of explanation is called for. Here and there are photographs which cannot be called technically perfect, but where the choice fell between the professionally taken, featureless, sales photograph and a print from a negative taken by one of the workmen using his Box Brownie, the latter won each time.

I have made no attempt to give technical details except in the mildest form; enthusiasts know them anyway, and whether the bore of a portable's cylinder was 8.25 or 7.6 cm is academic when it was broken up for scrap 50 years ago (by which time the bore was probably oval and varied between 8.25 and 7.6 cm anyway!). Again, it is modern practice to show horsepower in metric measurements, but which horsepower does one quote? Manufacturers used nominal horsepower (nhp). A big traction would be 5 nhp (literally, it could pull the same weight as five horses could); this is equivalent to 25 brake horsepower (or 40 bhp for short periods). The term 'horsepower' today seems extremely old fashioned; even in 1829 protests arose over the use of the word 'horsepower'. As *The Mechanics Magazine* said that year:

> How can we with any propriety continue talking of the horsepowers of engines, which exhibit performances that as far transcend the powers of the horse as the strength of the horse does that of the dog?

Therefore, the figures I quote are purely comparative.

I know you will enjoy this book, and please come and see, smell and hear the inherent beauty of the steam machines at your local rally.

It is with pleasure that I acknowledge the assistance given to me by R.W. Kidner, whose encyclopaedic memory eliminated many problems; R.H. Clark; Dennis Cook; Eric Fenton; James Gilbey; Tony Pierce; E.G. Pike; Frank D. Simpson; M. Thackrah; David Webster; Kevin Lane, who prepared the photographs; Tore Blom of Götene, Sweden; Lawrence R. Gibbs of Stillwater, Oklahoma, America; R.H. Johnston of Johannesburg, South Africa; Menno L. Kliewer of Reedley, California, America; John Norris of Beaufort, Victoria, Australia; Mrs A.S. Elsom, Bass Museum; A.N. King, Peter Brotherhood Ltd; M.J.B. Lovegrove, Chartered Insurance Institute; C.B. Brinkman, Charringtons Solid Fuel; R.F. Currie, Editor, *Classic Motor Cycle*; Brian Woolley, Archivist, EMAP; D.C. Phillips, Archivist, Institute of Agricultural History; Ian McMurtrie, Lothian & Borders Fire Brigade; A.E. Tomlinson, Marstons Brewery; Mrs F.E. Scott, National Trust for Scotland; Paul Goodman, Science Museum, London; N. Williams, Uralia Press; and my colleagues in the N.T.E.T. My greatest debt is to my wife, who like all girl-Fridays, gets all the blame and little of the praise.

Notes and anecdotes

The design of the steam machines for road use was constrained by the then current Highways Acts. By 1878 speeds of 2 mph (3.2 kph) in town and 4 mph (6.4 kph) in the countryside were permitted; councils were then empowered to make local bye-laws to govern road traffic, thus adding more problems. Some prohibited movement except in the hours of darkness and some vice versa; some authorities limited mileage to 5 miles (8 km) a day and some required the machine to get off the road whenever a horse approached. Licences were introduced – Worcestershire charged the maximum £10 per annum but reduced it to £5 if a licence was held for the neighbouring county. Day tickets to travel around the country cost ten shillings (50p)–a labourer's weekly wage. The year 1896 saw the 'man in front' restriction lifted and the 1903 Motor Car Act raised the speed limit to 5 mph (8 kph) for vehicles under five tons.

As limits changed so steamer designs evolved, although the 1933 Traffic Act was so biased against steam lorries that many were scrapped long before they were worn out. Reduced sales then led to a lack of capital for development and instead of modern steamers we are faced with diesel lorries, consuming foreign fuel instead of British–what might have been, given a little encouragement, can only be guessed from the illustrations.

Take the tram to town

Horse trams were welcomed by the public, but as the degree of cruelty caused to the horses became apparent so protests arose. Although the Victorians tolerated such illegal practices as dog and cock fights, the Victorian middle class would not accept blatant maltreatment of horses. Horses were normally bought in their prime (4–5 years old); hauling an omnibus they could work for $4\frac{1}{2}$ to 5 years, but a tram crippled them long before, 'making them fit only for the cats'-meat man'. In hilly terrain, no horse could work a tram more than, roughly, 18 miles (30 km) per day. In due course pressure was brought upon Parliament and in 1873 a Select Committee recommended that:

'... self-contained locomotive carriages (or engines), not exceeding six tons in weight, making no sound from their blast and consuming their own smoke ... be permitted to travel at the ordinary speed of vehicles drawn by horses, and be only subject to the same restrictions'.

Would-be promoters and engine manufacturers quickly moved in, and eventually at least 532 engines were running over a network of about 400 miles (650 km). It has been estimated that in all (including export orders), around 1200 steam tramway locomotives were built in Britain between 1873 and 1905.

Basically, a steam tram consisted of a mini-railway locomotive which hauled one or more trailers. Trams suffered from a number of physical defects, and as they had both a small boiler and very small wheels they slipped at the slightest provocation. They were heavy on the track, although later

7

models were surprisingly reliable. Comfort for the passengers was non-existent, for the bogies were generally unsprung; the seating wooden and, in early cars at least, longitudinal on the upper deck; in addition, the upper deck was often unglazed. There was no provision for heating, although some journeys could exceed an hour. Despite the strictest regulations (imposed through byelaws) governing how these trams were operated, complaints were unceasing. People complained about smoke, steam, noise, bad-timekeeping ('bunching', as practised by today's diesels, was a favourite cause for criticism), 'furious' and 'reckless' driving, overloading and 'insolent conduct'.

Another serious problem was water leakage: trams required replenishment of both water and coke at regular intervals and water dribbling from the hydrants or overflowing from the tanks froze in winter, making the roads slippery and dangerous for horse traction and pedestrians alike. The byelaws that controlled the trams' operation usually included a speed limit ('not exceeding 8 miles (13 km) per hour'), demanded they stopped on request ('when required by any passenger desiring to leave the car or to board it')–there were no bus stops. On top of the councils' requirements the Board of Trade had their rules, including specifications for fitted brakes, a governor to check speed, a bell and a bright light at night. Additionally, 'Whenever it is necessary to avoid impending danger, the engine shall be brought to a Standstill.'

The South Staffordshire Tramways Company network eventually totalled 22 miles (35 km) and provided services from Handsworth (Birmingham) to West Bromwich, Wednesbury, Walsall and Bloxwich, and at one time 38 locomotives and 34 trailers were owned. The oldest locomotives were built by one of the foremost engine manufacturers in the country, Beyer Peacock, to the patented design of William Wilkinson. These engines had a vertical boiler and the final drive was by cog-wheels. They were light, neat and reasonably efficient, and very favourable opinions for their future were entertained by many tramway engineers. They were also, at £600 each, value for money.

In the case of the South Staffordshire Tramways Compay the locomotives were perhaps too cheap, for although not delivered in 1883, by March 1886 the Handsworth Council was writing to the Board of Trade to ban steam trams in the area because:

> they make a great noise and clatter, emit large quantities of smoke and steam. The engine drivers say that the engines are badly constructed and in bad repair and they cannot stop them emitting smoke for these reasons.

Each locomotive ran about 20,000 miles (32,000 km) per year. There were undoubtedly problems with the different locomotives, and an interesting comparative table was published in 1893 (*opposite*).

Some idea of how much tramway parts cost can be gained from figures provided by Birmingham & Midland Tramways Ltd, in their annual report ending 30 June 1886. Engine miles in the year totalled 201,784; passengers carried amounted to 3,022,232 (an average of 15 passengers per mile, probably about 18 after eliminating empty running). The maintenance of the permanent way, mainly trackwork and making good the roadway had cost £96,314 – roughly £5500/km. The 22 engines had cost £17,330 (£788 each) and the 22 coaches £5127 (£233 each). It was understandable

Comparative locomotive costs for tramways in the Midlands

Company	System	Total cost per car per mile old pence	(new pence)
South Staffordshire	Steam	7.04	(2.93)
	Electric	4.06	(1.69)
Birmingham & Midland	Steam	7.83	(3.26)
Dudley & Stourbridge	Steam	8.57	(3.57)
Birmingham Central	Steam	6.79	(2.83)
	Electric Accumulator	11.59	(4.83)
	Cable	4.06	(1.76)

that one did not casually invest in operating steam trams. Here the expenditure – without wages – was, in round figures, £120,000 before any income accrued.

Although the locomotive of a steam tram set was itself reversible it had to be positioned at the leading end of the trailer; propelling was strictly forbidden. Therefore, unlike the self-contained electric car, the operation was complicated by the necessity of providing either reversing triangles or run round loops at the termini.

'After arrival at Snow Hill, Wolverhampton, the engine would uncouple, run forward a short distance and take water from a hydrant box sunk in the roadway. While this was going on, the driver would lift up the side flaps and oil the engine. After this, it ran round the car and coupled-up at the other end; connection was by central draw-and-buffer coupler .... There was also a coupling for the brakes and a communicating cord for signalling between conductor and driver. Periodically, the tram would stop at the depot beyond Sedgley and a

change of engine was made, so that fire cleaning and refuelling could be carried out. After that, the engine stood ready for the next change'.

Whatever their merits, and they were undeniable, both regulations and this complicated working prevented the development of steam tramways. Thus it is not really surprising that electric vehicles supplanted the steamers so quickly. Figure 13 purports to show 'the last steam car in England', pictured on 20 July 1909. There are a poignant few lines written on the back of the photograph:

Through storm and shine, I've run my race,
Electric cars now take my place,
For twenty years you've heard my bell,
But best of friends must say 'farewell'.

Dirty, dented and outdated, still someone appreciated that it was the last one they would ever see.

A few steam tramways were never electrified, and the Wolverton & Stony Stratford

Company was finally eliminated by the General Strike of 1926, although it was on the verge of collapse before then. Its claim to fame rests upon two factors: the use of the largest passenger cars (100 seaters) in Britain and its low fares. It was normal practice for the workmen at the LNWR Wolverton Works to go home to Stony Stratford for lunch, and so approximately 600 people had to be transported four times daily the 2½ miles (4 km) for a total of one shilling (5 p) each per week! Steam, and steam alone, made this possible.

By bus from city to country

The story of steam passenger vehicles on the road in Britain is one of individuals and later, small firms, battling against impossible odds. When the first attempts were made to run passenger-carrying vehicles on public highways, they ran foul of poor technology, blatant alarmist propaganda and, to some extent, ill-chosen routes. Yet steam power was a very real threat to the stage-coach industry in the same way that the railways were a far more effective form of transport than steam-powered vehicles. Steam offered an alternative to the complexities and man-power involved in running stage coaches. For a medium-sized coach stables, for instance, with 33 coaches (an average size for any main route in England) 709 horses were required. Each horse had a working life of three years and needed harness, horse shoes, hay, corn and straw. On average 87 men were needed to work as ostlers, stable-hands and administrators. The total expenditure including tolls was in excess of £64,000 a year – and that in 1840 when wages for a farm worker rarely exceeded 80 p a week. And there was a stage like this roughly every 10 miles (15 km). In

all it has been estimated that at least 150,000 horses were involved in stage coaching and some 50,000 people, of whom 17,000 were coachmen and guards.

Thus, when Sir Goldsworthy Gurney introduced plans to run vehicles from London to Bath, and slightly later, Walter Hancock planned a route from London to Birmingham, the stage-coach industry was horrified. The destruction of jobs and the many vested interests prompted an angry outcry from the many people concerned.

The early pioneers of steam transport, however, were venturing into unknown territory. Their metallurgical knowledge was limited and their quality control, with nearly all parts brought in, negligible. But at a time when most steam engines, marine and stationary alike, worked at 20–25 pounds per square inch (psi), the boilers designed by these men rose as high as 250 psi – a figure that even now is a matter requiring skilled, or at least accurate, workmanship.

Gurney, the first of the real bus men, started his experiments in 1824, initially using legs (or propellers), although later he discovered that wheels gave satisfactory adhesion. By 1828 his 14-seater 'Royal Patent' coach made its first, and possibly only, attempt to run from London to Bath. It failed. Its unsprung weight – 4 tons – a water consumption of 10 gallons per mile (30 litres per km) and rough roads, which defeated its cranked rear axle, led to its being horse-drawn. Interestingly, there was no provision for brakes and so the engine was reversed before descending any hills. Later, Gurney abandoned coaches and turned to steam tractors or drags – in effect self-contained locomotives.

A claim by steam coach operators that, having 6 in. (15 cm) wide tyres, their vehicles caused less damage to road surfaces than galloping hooves and narrow wheels was arguable. The Turnpike Trusts not only disputed this but also, faced with successful running by Sir Charles Dance with his steam drags of Gurney manufacture between Gloucester and Cheltenham (four times daily), they strewed the road with loose stones about 18 in. (46 cm) thick. These stones caused the coach to overturn and damage its mechanism.

Towards the end of his experiments Gurney had greatly improved upon the smoothness of the ride:

> ... [I] have used my carriage both on snow and on ice. On ice, a little roughing of the wheels is necessary, in the same manner as you rough horses, and little power is sufficient to propel the carriage, because under those circumstances the power necessary to draw the weight is considerably reduced, and therefore the full power of the engine is not necessary to be exerted: in deep snow, there is great difficulty; but I have no doubt that as the subject goes on improving, all those particular difficulties will be overcome.

On a good road he had reached 20–30 mph (32–48 kph) but reckoned to cruise at 12 mph (19.3 kph).

Walter Hancock was a man of great ingenuity. After he had made his first steam carriage reliable he then merely produced updated models, adding to his knowledge rather than trying a different direction. He used a two-speed mechanism, seemingly something like the chain-driven gear of a bicycle. Steering was still a problem, for so-called 'Ackerman's steering' was not available and so he used a centre pin not dissimilar to that of a child's pull-along toy but fitted with a foot-controlled damper. Hancock understood, as many later engineers had to re-discover, the secret of a working engine. They are, he said:

> completely protected from the dirt and dust of the roads; are at all times in sight of the engineer, and every part of them is within his reach. The passengers, engines, boiler, fire-place, &c., are all equally relieved from concussion, by complete suspension on springs.

His boiler was probably one of the safest built in the period. This was proved when one of his steamers stopped suddenly and Hancock 'went to the engineer to ask him why this was:

> He told me he had not stopped the carriage; and he immediately applied his hand to the gauge cocks, and found there was neither steam nor water in the boiler. I immediately knew that the boiler had burst. They (the passengers) said they did not know it, as they heard no noise, I told them I did not mean they should know it.

It turned out there were four holes in the boiler large enough to put his hand through.

One of Hancock's journeys in 1835 makes interesting reading; although the journey time was in no way comparable with that of Brunel's railway, it was excellent compared with the horse-drawn coach.

Journey time from London to Malborough by steam road coach

	No. of miles	Miles from London	Time		Stoppages		Time of travelling exclusive of stoppages		Miles per hour	[Kilometres per hour]
			h.	m.	h.	m.	h.	m.		
AM										
London	0	0	6	27						
Hounslow	10	10	7	27	0	8	0	53	11.3	18.2
Maidenhead	16	26	9	37	0	41	1	29	10.8	17.4
Reading	13	39	11	11	0	13	1	21	9.6	15.4
Dine at Reading					1	20				
PM										
Newbury	17	56	3	11	0	54	1	46	9.6	15.4
Marlborough	19	75	6	23	0	50	2	22	8.0	12.9
Total	75		11	54	4	6	7	49	9.6	15.4

The return journey was performed in roughly equal time.

In all it is known that Hancock built nine machines with varied seating:

Experimental carriage	4 outside
Infant (trunnion engines)	10 outside
Ditto (enlarged with fixed engines)	14 outside
Era (Greenwich)	16 inside, 2 out
Enterprise	14 inside
Autopsy	9 inside, 5 out
Erin	8 inside, 6 out
German Drag	6 outside, exclusive of those accommodated in the separate carriages behind
Automaton	22 outside

The crew invariably consisted of steersman, engineer and fireman.

Although Hancock was an ingenious engineer, he was no businessman; in 1836 even though his vehicles (according to his own account) carried over 12,500 passengers, he was eventually let down so badly by outsiders that he abandoned any future plans.

The most successful working during this period was not in England, but Scotland, where coaches left both Glasgow and Paisley on the hour every daylight hour for seven months in 1834 and could well have continued to do so. Six 26-seater vehicles were used, built to the design of Sir John Scott Russell. But the turnpike operators were determined to finish steam coaches and they succeeded. In 1834 they heaped loose stones on the road, so that the wheel, proving unequal to the strain of dragging itself over the stones, forced the full weight of the coach onto a corner of the rectangular boiler. Five passengers died, 12 were injured and although the Turnpike Trustees admitted their guilt in court the service had to be withdrawn.

Among the plans to build steam vehicles was one extraordinary idea, which contemporary reports claim actually worked. It was a traction engine running inside a 10 ft (3 m) wheel, like a hamster in a cage. The carriage followed along behind.

Considering that the 'big wheel' was iron and driven by gears, the unholy din did little for the reputation of steam. Opposition to steam vehicles came also from scientists who were quick to point out fallacious claims. In 1829 Sir James C. Anderson and W.H. James jointly patented a coach design which included 'separate engines' to drive by gears each wheel of the vehicles. A reviewer pointed out that:

> to call each separate cylinder a separate engine because the cylinders can 'act together or separately', is just about as proper as it would be to call each leg of a horse a horse, since they also can act together or separately. There are many other things which are essentially component parts of a steam-engine cylinder ... when next he [James] talks of putting a whole engine in his pocket, he ought to add all but – the furnace, the flue, the chimney, the boiler, the casings, the pumps, the frame-work, &c.

Roughly a century later, Sentinel recommended the use of only tap water for their lorry boilers to solve the problem of scale. Mr James tackled the problem in a different way in 1829: he thought that if the boiler was made to revolve and marbles were placed in the tubes then the sediment could be washed out easily. Yet someone wisely pointed out:

> the incrustations which will take place in tubes of three quarters of an inch in diameter, under a temperature of many hundred degrees, will indurate so quickly, that unless he repeats his hurdy-gurdy process every twenty-four hours at least, we suspect he will find himself at last literally playing at marbles.

Complexity of cars

One of the first successful steam cars was built by Colonel R.E. Crompton (famous as a maker of electrical components) while he was stationed in India. Objecting to the lifestyle where most of his brother officers were 'accustomed to spend a large part of the day in bed ....' he decided to put together an engine and by 1867 had a vehicle running. Problems soon manifested themselves: he was plagued by broken crankshafts and also suffered from clinkering of the firebars as the fuel was briquettes made up of charcoal dust and cowdung.

This vehicle, or most of it, is still extant but on returning to England the Colonel moved on to a White steam car. Built in 1901, of a nominal 6 hp, this vehicle was hard worked, running as many as 232 miles in a day from London to Yorkshire. Colonel Crompton reminisced that, 'On the run in question [I] ... started at 5 o'clock in the morning from Kensington Court, and reached Tanfield, near Bedale, at 8 o'clock the same evening–a distance of 232 miles – with only one filling of petrol and one filling of water'. This might not seem remarkable today but in 1902 not only were road

13

surfaces made of loose stone and grit, but there were no kerbs, nor 'cats'-eyes', the springing was minimal, there was no provision for wind protection and the steering by tiller was rudimentary. In the three years of ownership the White had run 'upwards of 60,000 miles'.

Similar cars were made commercially available. The 10 hp car of 1903 cost £420 if paid for in cash, although hire purchase terms comprising £112 deposit and 12 monthly payments of £28.25 were available. For this you received '... a steam generator that is not a boiler and is indestructable' [an optimistic claim], an aluminium body, two sets of brakes [in 1903!] and a special condenser. It was, the American manufacturers claimed, '... the nearest approach to an absolutely ideal motor car that has yet been produced'.

There were other steam cars available by the turn of the century. A thoroughly British steam car, the Lamplough-Albany, whistled across the stage in 1903, at a price of £598.50 – an impossible figure for a steamer–and drifted quietly away. On the other hand £430.50 would buy a Miesse, once Belgian but now made in England by the Turner Manufacturing Company of Wolverhampton. Ingenious in design and after 1907 shaft driven, they were catalogued until 1913. Around 1904 however, there were three steamers that could rival the White for reliability and advanced features: the New English Serpollet; the Locomobile; and the Stanley. Also the Toledo, in its last year of manufacture, came in a number of guises at various prices from the Doctor's Phaeton 7½ hp for £260 to the 'new 10 hp Loco 'Toledo Surrey' at £375. The main advantage of a Toledo was that below the boiler fire level there was a sludge tank into which, hopefully, the grit and dirt held in water extracted from a village pond or brook would settle and be blown out at night. The retention of tiller steering no matter how free from vibration, told against it, although the auxiliaries were well designed and efficient. The tyres, called Endurance Diamond, were made from 'compound rubberine jelly', which was patented as a sort of magical substance that 'instantly closes all punctures under air pressure'. The claim, unfortunately, deflated with the tyres.

The year 1930 saw the end of the Locomobile by which time it had changed from a relatively simple Stanley look-alike, fragile and temperamental, really only fit for a gentle ride along Hyde Park on a summer's day, to a solid workmanlike vehicle with proper lubrication, superheated steam, adequate brakes, a speed of 38 mph (61 kph) and a range of 30 miles (48 km) per tank of water. But Stanley saw the oncoming demise and turned from making a petrol-fired steam car to a petrol-fired internal combustion car. Stanley continued producing these until 1925, while Doble, perhaps the most sensible of all steam manufacturers concentrated on expensive, exclusive models, only producing four a year at a price as high as a Rolls Royce.

Steam cars never really had much of a life or indeed posed very much of a threat to the emergent petrol vehicle industry as, despite their silence, they were too complex and too short-ranged. In round figures out of the 200 makers (of whom only 30 were British) who made steam vehicles between 1890 and 1920, 150 were out of business by 1904 and 50 were extant, but half of those survived only by grace of First World War fuel shortages.

A pro-steam writer of 1904 summed up steam vehicles when he said that although they were strongly built, sweet and silent in running,

they are not suitable for excessive speeds ... and they have ... certain mild disabilities–such as the necessity for watchfulness in driving, in lubrication, and because of the presence of a fire – that in a curious way tends to restrict their use pleasantly to moderate journeys instead of hurried and, in the end, expensive, long-distance, non-stop runs ... the whole management of the two [petrol and steam] is different; a more loving, more personal care is necessary for steam; it needs more delicate and imaginative handling; its disorders are slighter, less obscure, more human than those of the petrol engine. It takes longer actually to prepare a steam car for the road than it takes to prepare a petrol car ....

In other words they were slower and required more time to prepare. But the private car owner has always wanted speed, then and now!

The other problem was that steamers could be messy. Neville Grenville, whose car, which still works but is now in the Bristol Museum, wrote in his diary:

Tue. Apr.7 1896 – Mr Pinney came at 9.30 am and we started with the steam carriage at 9.45. George Mildred with me in front, Mr Noble firing, Mrs NG and Mrs Audrey with us as far as the Horse and Lion; on through Glastonbury and to Polsham; stopped there for five buckets of water, and on to Wells, arriving at the Palace at 10.50 – ten miles in 65 minutes, including stops for water, horses and a railway level crossing. Called on the Bishop as promised ... someone thought I was a bagman come to sell the carriage to the Bishop ....

Magnificent motorcycles

Steam two- and three-wheelers were not a success but in their lifetime went full circle. In 1881 there appeared a steam tricycle built to the patented design of Sir Thomas Parkyns by Arthur Bateman, an engineer of Greenwich, London:

These were the dark days when the law demanded that motor vehicles or steam carriages, as they styled them – having traction engines in mind – should only be driven when the wheels were 4 in. wide, when there were three men in attendance, two on the machine, and one ahead carrying a ref flag, the pace not to exceed two miles an hour. It need not be pointed out that with this machine it was impossible to fulfil the first two conditions, so the inventor was fined 1s (5p) for breaking the law. He appealed to the Queen's Bench, but the appeal was dismissed, the Act stating that any vehicle 'propelled other than by animal power' came under the heading of 'steam carriage'.

James Saddler, a man of great ingenuity, fitted a Locomobile engine and boiler to a motorcycle combination. In 1937 (56 years after the Parkyns machine) a reviewer wrote that 'I left with feelings of regret that steam has been so neglected as a means of comfortable motoring on three or even two wheels'. Control was by a steam valve giving a 'feeling of extreme power ... if one wished to stop, one simply reversed the [forward and reverse] lever and braked on the engine ...'. The boiler, paraffin-fired, operated at 400 psi, the tank held 8 gallons (36 litres) of fuel and the water tank 10 gallons (45 litres) giving a range of 200 miles (320

15

km); of especial note was its 'four-cylinder miniature steam engine with a bore and stroke of 25.5 x 25.5 mm [which] drives the dynamo'.

In the years 1900 to 1920, were many makes, some reaching production, others lurching from drawing board to bankruptcy, with only a few (if any) machines ever reaching the roads. One contemporary writer stated that the parts of his steam cycle that did not actually melt, glowed red-hot, broke or burst into flames.

One valiant attempt at production was made by Pearson & Cox, whose model was manufactured from 1911 to 1913. In theory the Pearson & Cox should have been a good machine as the company's cars were relatively successful, but by 1913 they had sold out to the Steam Cycle & Motor Company who renamed the motorcycle the Dawn. The starting of a steam cycle was far more complex than that of its rival, the motor cycle:

A special case on the carrier holds a small blow-lamp and a reserve methylated spirit container, each of which holds about half a pint of spirit. Having lit the blow-lamp, one hooks it on to the side of the generator, from which position its flame is directed straight on to the burner. About 30 psi, air pressure having been produced in the paraffin tank by the hand pump and the burner sufficiently heated, the paraffin vapour valve is open and the burner lighted, this procedure taking about five minutes. The Bowden ratchet lever is then pushed downwards three-quarters of its travel and if the machine is pushed at walking pace it will start in its own length. The lever is opened till the desired speed is attained, and the machine can be checked immediately or

stopped by raising a lever on the left bar, which allows any steam in the generator to pass into the tank immediately. It may be thus gathered that simplicity of control is one of the Dawn's salient features.

Sent for review in the January of 1914, 'the model we saw was not quite complete in one or two details'; the First World War interceded and the Dawn never rose.

Utilitarian portables

The portable is the ancestor of all steam road vehicles. The name is rather a misnomer, however, as their portability was limited to their wheels and shafts which enabled a horse or pair of donkeys to move them from site to site. Their nominal horse power varied from one to nine, and the smallest size usually ran a sawmill, water pumps or grist mill to provide chicken meal. Sometimes they were also used to operate a bone grinder, although 3 hp was the recommended size for this, as it was for a potato riddler. The very small sizes have an almost elfin charm, standing no higher than a man and often supporting an immensely tall and attentuated chimney. Conversely, the larger sizes tend to look like tractions that have shed their driving wheels and steering mechanism, a fate which in fact overcame some older, slower, single-geared tractions when they were superseded by modern machines for front line duty.

Some firms, Clayton & Shuttleworth in particular, and Marshall and Garrett, made thousands of portables, especially for export to the colonies. Other foundries met a local need, producing machines of the required power and thereby giving, in the long term, better value for money. In a typical 'rural' boiler, tubes would be $2\frac{1}{2}$ in (6 cm) diameter rather than 2 in (5 cm), this not only made them free steamers but reduced scaling problems where hard water was the norm, albeit at a higher fuel cost.

Portables consumed fuel voraciously, and the boilers therefore had to be robust. Where the plates were made by hand and a constant temperature could be maintained, the flanges were stronger. On the other hand, factory-made plates were made with hydraulic presses, which put pressure on the sheets and often caused cracking. Thus the machines which were made locally and by hand had a longer boiler life on the whole.

Basically agricultural machines (although some were modified for use inside factories and as pumping engines), portables had little cause to be out and about on the roads unless owned by a co-operative of farmers.

Controls and fittings were necessarily of the simplest; single cylinders were adequate. In Britain it was normal practice for the belt to be taken off the flywheel, although on the Continent twin flywheels or a suitable diameter pulley were used. There were surprisingly few recorded accidents, although boiler inspections and insurance were unknown. Generally there would be a local man who understood any ailments over and above leaking glands or tubes, which a labourer could repair with red lead and packing plus a roughly fitting drift. It was not always the blacksmith, for in my village an elderly local chauffeur would oblige, although even he drew a line at an ancient Ransomes, Sims & Jefferies that had been resurrected during the war and whose firebox wheezed in and out like an old man's chest.

In the heyday of portables any reasonable sized farm possessed one or more, even if thrashing was left to the contractor and his traction engine. Yet again the flood of American equipment made available in the First World War first undermined sales (supplies were in any event rather short) and later led to their being put to one side. The 'oil' engine, powered by a variety of fuels but primarily petrol or paraffin, was at once less demanding of manpower, available (theoretically) at the swing of a handle, and consumed a fuel already required for the new farm tractors.

Heavy metal

The land tractor was a last desperate attempt by steam vehicle manufacturers to compete with the Fordson and its kin for hauling implements. Obviously, the handful of machines made rarely ventured onto the highway and even the one photograph (fig 49) used in this book was taken in a grassy field. This machine was the result of a gallant attempt to produce an economic, light and yet sturdy tractor. During the Second World War some rather unlucky attempts were made to plough acres of Essex clay using a 'traditional' lightweight Wallis & Steevens 'Oilbath' steam tractor. With the five-gang plough set at 14 in (35.6 cm) the whole front end reared up like some enormous beetle, and although she eventually went to work amid a series of explosive barks from the chimney, she ended up at the marshy bottom end of the field, resting on her ashpan, and was subsequently rescued by an elderly Field Marshal semi-diesel tractor.

In the early part of this century Mann, a company better known for its steam cars and lorries, endeavoured to adapt its design to perform as a land tractor. Unfortunately, relatively narrow wheels led to excessive slippage, not only on greasy soils but in the very conditions where they should have been most useful: during the harvest, even without a load, they would slip to a halt on cut straw. Then, too, there was the problem that a boy was required to fetch water not only to the threshing engine but the steam tractor bringing in the corn. But the Garrett 'Suffolk Punch' of 1917 was so nearly successful. The machine was relatively well balanced, it had good water consumption, was chain driven, and with a forward steering position, manoeuvrability was incomparable. Had it appeared a decade earlier the whole face of agriculture might have changed, but as it was direct ploughing by motor tractor received a boost from wartime conditions, as many thousands of American-built machines eventually flooded the market.

Brute force

For the sake of simplicity I have included in this category ballasted or extremely short wheelbase lorries which performed a similar function to today's motorized articulated lorry. Some heavy duty tractors were purpose-built, but it was more common to take a superannuated steam lorry still with plenty of life in it, shorten the wheelbase very considerably, add ballast (normally solid, often bullhead rail but water tanks were an alternative), sometimes modify the gear or chain sprocket ratios and reinforce the bumpers. Occasionally solid tyres were retained; these would sometimes slip on the greasy slime overlaying the cobbles of the fish dock where the girls were busily cleaning the fish but it was unusual to see the wheels rotate inside the tyres. Conversely, where pneumatics were fitted, one or two of the poorer firms tried to economize here – following a grossly overloaded Sentinel tractor once, I saw square blocks of rubber being left behind where the tread had been recut once too often, or cheaply remoulded in the first place.

A 'pure' tractor was quite different. Sentinel offered a specialized timber tractor and in the 1940s many of the vehicle paths through forests were surfaced with split trees laid across the direction of travel. To see one of these tractors lurching up and down with every conceivable loosepart setting up an unbelievable cacophany and yet still hauling, on solid tyred bogies, three or four fully grown oak trunks each 39–45 ft (10–15 m) long was to see the power of steam. And, again, one day at the Elephant & Castle in London, a Foden tractor, probably a C-type, and at least 25 years old, was beavering away hauling around 20 tons of tramway for some renewal scheme. Owing to recent bombing there were still soft spots in the road surface and occasionally she would roll into one and yet, creaking and groaning, emerge to plod on.

Steam leaks were very common apparently in tractors, and yet the driver who had, of course, to be part-time stoker appeared utterly unperturbed. But the release and sale of ex-services AEC Matadors and the like at very low prices in 1945–46 more or less finished these giants; convenience overrode any sentimental attachment.

Ubiquitous lorries

Steam lorries or waggons occupied, for a brief while, the position of the motor goods vehicle. From 1890 to 1910 there were about 75 manufacturers in business, all vying for the same market. Some like Leyland and Foden went on to greater things; others like Musker and Brotherhood faded from the scene. Variations in the position of the boiler and engine were as manifold as the makers and the engine bodies. Petrol (in cans) and ammunition were carried as often as peas, potatoes and timber.

One specialised form of flatbed lorry was the brewers' dray; orders for these were eagerly sought after by all the leading manufacturers. Generally these steamers appear to have been hard worked and well maintained–owing to the breweries' high standards, the paintwork and cleanliness was often as much an advertisement for the makers as the customers. Typically, Marstons, the Burton brewers, bought theirs in batches, two Fodens in 1912–13, three Clayton & Shuttleworth in 1915 and, lastly, two Sentinels in ? The last steamer, FA 3800, was sold off in 1937.

Test runs to establish the economy of the steam lorry were held on the Sentinels in 1929 and records have survived at Marstons.

Journey: Burton-on-Trent to Southampton, 150 miles (241 km)
Load carried: 60 barrels in 36 gallon casks, 12 ton (12,192 kg)
Weight of wagon: 9 ton (9145 kg)
With fuel and water gross weight: 23 ton 4 cwt (23,700 kg)
Actual driving: $8\frac{1}{4}$ hours
Average speed: 29.45 mph (18.3 kph)
On top of this water stops totalled 39 minutes and meal breaks $1\frac{1}{2}$ hours; total journey time was, therefore, 10 hours, 35 minutes.

Return Journey
Load carried: 60 empty barrels
Actual driving hours: 7 hours 2 minutes
Average speed: 34.59 mph (21.5 kph)
Water stops 33 minutes, meal breaks $1\frac{1}{2}$ hours; total journey time was, therefore, 9 hours, 25 minutes.

The fuel used (either coal or coke) for the outward journey was 10 cwt (at 38/6d a ton), costing 19/3d. For the return journey it was 9 cwt, costing 17/4d. The total cost of fuel and oil was £1.11.11 (outward) and £1.0.0 (return) So the cost per barrel, including return of empties, exclusive of all charges except fuel and oil was about $8\frac{1}{2}$ d (3.54 p).

Driving a steam waggon was hard work; even before firing up, the bits and pieces of dunnage had to be checked:
'2 buckets, Brasso, Rags, Screwdriver, 5 gallons oil [22.7 litres] Stilsons [an adjustable spanner], Lagging and Paint, Wire Wool, 3 cwt [154 kg] Coal, Kindling & Chisel', were the official requirements laid down by one operator. This stowed away, lighting up time came next, and, according to Sentinels' own handbook, '... with proper care steam may be raised from cold water in 50 minutes ...'. But first the boiler had to be filled with 'pure and clean water ... use town or drinking water from the mains wherever possible'. The working water level in the boiler had to be 3 in (7.6 cm) from the bottom of the gauge glass. To check this it was necessary to 'Turn the three gauge cock handles horizontal, turn the top and bottom handles back again vertical, then turn the middle handle vertical, when the water should rise to working level'.

Fuel, ideally, was coke – but it had to be sieved; then, and only then, could the fireman light the fire:

Unhook ashpan, tilt firegrate, clean both and replace, half filling ashpan with water. Lift furnace door on boiler top, light some shavings or waste soaked in paraffin and throw down on to grate. Follow with plenty of firewood until there is a good blaze and a thick fire. Spread a layer of coke on top and when red hot add more slowly, spreading it well from time to time.

19

Then the fireman had to test the injector, warm the cylinders (gently) and, to ensure adequate lubrication, 'while steam is blowing through cylinder work the small force feed oil pump by hand for about twenty strokes'. The driver, meanwhile, theoretically at least, greased the axle journals, checked the oil level in the crankcase and refilled if required, drained off and refilled the cam shaft wheel case, oiled the chain, reversing and steering gears, and greased all 17 nipples. That was daily. Other jobs were called for weekly, fornightly and monthly, together with a boiler wash-down on the 'Free' day (usually Saturday).

Docker Brothers, a paint manufacturer of Ladywood, Birmingham used a steam waggon in the 1930s in a typical way. One of their products was used in the making of brake linings by Ferodo of Chapel-en-le-Frith. Before the purchase of a Sentinel, delivery by rail took a week and involved shipment by road to and from the railheads. The Sentinel was fitted with two 3410 litre (750 gallon) tanks and could complete the journey in a day. The driver, Ben Ward, was very proud of his engine which, among other extras, was fitted with a water pan under the engine to catch the hot embers. Water was collected on the route at a pond, the measure being that you should have enough steam to climb the Derbyshire hills. Hours for a driver were 7.30 am until 6 pm with an hour break for lunch and they were paid 10 shillings a day in 1935.

The Sentinel was disposed of during the early part of the war. By 1940, drivers' wages in Devon stood at £3.10s a week, while a stoker on a Sentinel DG 6 received $87\frac{1}{2}$ d a week for working 7 am to any time after 5 pm and Saturdays 7 am to 1 pm. Despite the hard work these were adventur-

ous times; drivers were tested by the degree of concentration required and the task of gauging when a machine needed water and where it was to be found. One driver remembers an interesting case:

We were travelling along a road when I noticed the water glass was nearly empty. Bert Cross, the driver, said 'I think we are out of water!'. The next place for taking on water was about two miles away. When we got there I got the hose out and was walking around the front of the wagon to the stream when, suddenly, there was an explosion, and lots of steam. Being new at the job I wondered what was happening, as you can imagine. Of course, we had lost the [fusible] plug, but within about 15 minutes everything was quiet and peaceful again.

This stoker's most frightening experience came later and was coupled with another incident which proved the gross overloads possible with a steam lorry:

We and another lorry took two loads of nissan hutting to an army detachment stationed in the grounds of Sherbourne Castle. We had unloaded our hutting, and at about 3 pm had started to load up another load from Sherbourne for Dunster Beach, when the air raid siren went, and about 150 German planes suddenly appeared overhead and dropped bombs and land mines. (Eighteen people died in Sherbourne that day, from the raid.) Meanwhile, the two drivers, two ATS girls and two grooms (who happened to be passing by), the other stoker and I, dived for the shelter of our waggon and managed to get underneath, this being the nearest place for cover. I remember looking out between the rear wheels of the wagon watching the bombs land in the lake, about 200 yards [183 metres] away. The earth seemed to lift beneath us as each bomb dropped. I'd noticed that not all of the bombs had exploded and when the castle lake was dredged a couple of years ago, they were found. We finished loading the two lorries the next day and started our trip home. On our way I said to Bert, 'The waggon doesn't seem to be pulling well.' We didn't have much coal left – mainly dust, and about 50 lb [psi] of steam. By this time we'd reached the bottom of a long hill approaching Ilminster. We stopped in a lay-by with just enough steam to fill the boiler up with water. When we had a look around the wagon I could see why she was not pulling well. The rear spring hangers were rubbing on the four rear tyres with the weight of the load.

It turned out that this vehicle was carrying 30 tons when its specified payload was 10 tons.

Any driver of any steam waggon made a mistake at some time, but bearing in mind the narrowness of roads even in the 1930s, the lack of markings and the mixture of vehicles, it is surprising there were not more. It was a quite usual, although extremely dangerous, practice for steam vehicles to speed up a downhill journey by putting her 'out of gear'. One driver recalls such an occasion:

> One day we came unstuck. Going past the Stags Head Inn, as usual out of gear, just as we pulled out to pass a horse and putt loaded with corn, another truck appeared from a dip in the road – hidden by overgrown trees. My driver slammed the waggon back into top gear and full reverse. But it was too late, we either had

to hit the other truck or the cart. I can still picture the scene today with the driver of the cart nodding, half asleep, unaware of his imminent danger! We hit the cart on the rear offside corner. The poor horse finished on top of the hedge – still within the broken shafts. Even worse the carter, Mr Sedgebeer, finished up under the remains of the cart covered in corn. Luckily for us he only had a broken arm and the horse was OK.

Most coal carriers preferred tipping waggons and none more so than Charringtons. At Cable Street, London, in the 1920s, for example, where there was a mountain-range of coal, 'black peak upon peak, stretching along the big yard', the railway trucks discharged into shutes which poured directly into a hydraulically-tipped steam waggon. The scene was described as follows:

> Anything done with perfect skill born of long experience is fascinating to watch; the man who takes the heavy sack on his back, runs gaily up a springy board, and shoots the sack into the wagon makes the feat look what it is not, absurdly easy. So does the driver of the lorry, who backs it and then goes forward and then back again so precisely to accommodate the torrent of coal. In three minutes or so the lorry is full, and off it goes to deliver its load and comes back to get another and yet another. It can unload as swiftly as it loads. The driver pressed a lever and the lorry tips up its load and dumps it in the twinkling of an eye.

Maids of all work

Traction engines have been likened to the dinosaur, dying while still in their prime. They evolved from portables, the first self-moving engine being built in 1842, although steered by a horse in shafts. Jolting over bad roads wracked the boilers and frames of these early machines and they had a working life of only a year or two. In 1854 Boydell patents covered wheels equipped with flat, hinged plates to prevent them sinking into the soft ground and to increase grip on gravel surfaces. The system, a so-called 'endless railway' almost worked, but the design proved to be ahead of available technology. On one trip Boydell and his crew of seven took a load of 17 tons from Thetford in Norfolk to London in the three days from 14 to 16 May 1857. On the road the train was 122 ft (37.19 m) long, made up of the engine, a timber waggon, two threshing machines, another waggon carrying water and dunnage for the engine and a portable engine. However, en route problems soon became apparent. On the first day they left Thetford at 10.30 am, but by 1.43 they were forced to stop because of a heated driving wheel (a new box had been put in that morning). Later they ran out of steam because the coke had been too slow burning and had smothered the fire. By 5.30 the steering was playing up and by 7.36 the engine 'tended to the near watercourse [ditch] and at last got into it ...'. The first day's running took 10 hours 10 minutes; deducting stoppages they ran for 6 hours 35 minutes, giving an average speed of 3.4 mph (5.5 kph). On the Friday they rounded off the day by getting stuck in a dung-heap, and on the Saturday the main gear wheel lost some teeth and the crank-shaft was found to have slightly bent.

An alternative means of achieving traction was that devised by William Bray who arranged a system of retractable 'tongues' to protrude through the wheels, and offered his machine in a variety of guises. Both these designs were in some ways aberrations, and

the process of powering 'portable' farm engines, hitherto horsedrawn, was to be the next step by Thomas Aveling in 1858. His argument was that 'it is an insult to mechanical science, to see half-a-dozen horses drag along a steam engine, and the sight of six sailing vessels towing a steamer would certainly not be more ridiculous'. Initially the machine was steered by a fifth wheel, but by 1864 the traction engine we know today – gear-driven, water and fuel tanks an integral part of the engine, and steering by chain and bobbin – had arrived. Compounding, which in certain circumstances almost doubles the power from one cylinder full of steam, was invented in 1881, springing in 1875 and the differential (enabling one back wheel to go round a corner at a different speed to its mate) by 1890.

Carrying loads like coal had certain inherent problems, particularly in the days when a traction engine would be used to tow two or three ex-horse trailers into the poorer parts of the cities. Down by Poplar in London, children would hitch a ride on the back of the furthermost waggon until they were near their homes. One would then hop down and put a lump of wood under the back wheel, thus making the vehicle bounce on the cobbles and shed some of the load. It was almost obligatory for the driver to chase one conspicuous child while the rest of the gang scuttled off home with their booty. There was honour on both sides: 'the driver were a-chasin' one of us, he didn't see us take the coal, but we only collected what fell off 'cos that wasn't like stealing.'

Accustomed as we are now to pneumatically-tyred vehicles, it is difficult to remember the incredible din and vibration of iron shod, virtually unsprung, wheels, on a traction engine and its trailer when the latter was fully laden. Near Lord Street, Nechells, Birmingham, the main road was half tarmac and half cobbles and every day around 11 am a Foden traction and an iron-wheeled bogie bolster waggon laden with logs used to pass by on its way to the sawmill. As it passed:

> ... the grandfather clock in the parlour used to shift on the wall and stayed inaccurate until Father came home for lunch ... on its way back the wagon didn't seem to move it quite so much, so it only lost 5 minutes in the hour. Father put it right again in the evening!

On 2 December, 1880, there was a boiler explosion which killed the steersman. The engine, an 8 nhp Aveling & Porter, was completely wrecked, but it was found that the safety valves had been locked down to avoid blowing off steam as they went through Maidstone where the police were very strict. The load was what is euphemistically called 'night-soil', so the results carried a certain degree of poetic justice.

The result of a runaway traction is shown in figure 100. The engine is Fowler No. 1165, built in 1868, and the photograph dates back to around 1900. At the time she was owned by Ward & Dale of Sleaford and was en route from the village of Navenby near Lincoln to the GNR station to haul back a load. As she started to run down the hill, the friction band drive to one hind wheel slipped, despite having been adjusted the previous day, and with no alternative means of braking, the foreman, Bill Clark (on the left in the photograph) tried to decrease speed by rubbing against the verge. As can be seen, the accident was quite comprehensive but the engine was repaired quite quickly, and the machine

returned to ploughing. Although slightly outside the parameters of this book, it is worth noting that Ward & Dale were the last of the great steam ploughing contractors to survive; their tackle was auctioned off on 10 March, 1939. The machines sold that day were the mightiest, the most elegant and yet versatile ploughing engines of all, the Fowler BBs selling for between £50 and £140 a pair. Today they would fetch a thousand times that – and be no less attractive.

The work carried out by tractions was prodigious; indeed without steam vehicles Britain would never have achieved greatness, as before the motor lorry there was no alternative way to move the heavy machinery that was as economically viable. To give an example is easy. In 1899 the Army wished to move a load of 35 tons from Aldershot to a camp 60 miles (97 km) away. A traction engine required four men, used a ton of coal and took 22 hours to move this load, whereas by horse-power 70 horses were required, and no less than three officers, five NCOs and 35 men, all of whom had to be fed and watered for the three days they took to complete the journey.

In general, the simpler the traction engine mechanism, the better it survived: boiler life, given a good water district, was around 50 years; fireboxes lasted 10 to 12 years; and the gears could last 40 years if they were not lubricated with neat grit too often. There were probably a hundred or so makers extant at one time or another, varying from Corbett of Wellington, Shropshire, who built, at most, a handful, to J & H McLaren of Leeds whose works averaged ten machines a week.

Elsewhere in Europe, except Germany, tractions were never as well developed as in Britain; there were, therefore, many British manufacturers who had subsidiary European concerns, particularly Clayton & Shuttleworth (Budapest & Vienna) and Fowlers (Magdeburg). One exception to this was Sweden where 25 different works produced tractions, although only Munktells were of any significant size, with around 6500 portables and tractions on a 20:1 ratio being manufactured between 1853 and 1921. Munktells are now part of the Volvo group.

Similarly, exports to the colonies were once the mainstay of many companies; products were adapted to suit the climate and terrain, such as water trap ashpans, spark-arrester-fitted chimneys, increase clearances and fireboxes capable of burning peat, straw, sugar-cane or any other indigenous waste products. Companies also produced different-sized machines to suit America. The Best Manufacturing Company specialized in vertical boiler engines which dwarfed the Aveling & Porter equivalent, one logging model weighing 65 tons with the chimney's cap 20 ft (6 m) from the ground, while another maker, Benicia, produced driving wheels of 10 ft 6 in (3.2 m) in diameter. Such machines were proportionally more powerful too: 20 nhp was a normal output and 25 nhp (75 hp) in no way unusual. It is a salutary thought that while Britain had, at most, a hundred makers of tractions, one state alone in America, Minnesota, had 137 manufacturers, while Illinois came close with 123! It must be borne in mind, however, that Minnesota is not much smaller than Britain in size, although it is much less densely populated.

Steam supreme

As the expensive motor car is to the workaday delivery van, so was the showman's road locomotive to the traction engine. By the nature of their work they had to be strong, being required to haul heavy loads over rough roads and then to provide either direct power for a ride or electric power for virtually any operation. They were and are, fantastically attractive, some being as highly decorated as a canal narrow boat, but they always had a profusion of brass, gunmetal, copper and polished aluminium. The drivers of some even went so far as to burnish the rivets of their tool-boxes and water-tanks.

Not all showman's locomotives started life in the form that they were to attain later. Fowler 14425 of 1916, was used behind the trenches to haul ammunition waggons through the mud and muck of the Flanders countryside. Named, logically enough, 'Carry On', she was returned to England, converted to showman's standards and all 20 tonnes of her remain in service, at least on rally sites.

Many showman's locomotives were fitted with a Thompson-Walton 'Feast' single beam crane to the rear of the engine, thus allowing relatively rapid handling of heavy and awkward lumps of machinery. The work involved in assembling, and later dismantling, the quite complicated roundabouts and swing boats can easily be guessed.

The first recorded use of electric generation on a road locomotive was that by R.E.B. Crompton at the Henley Regatta in July 1879. The engine was a Marshall, and at a time when most houses still relied on oil or candles, it must have been an amazing spectacle. Perhaps not unsurprisingly there were those who regarded such an advance as the Devil's work and encouraged a drunken mob to attack the engine. A combination of steam and the strong Gainsborough arms of the men from Marshall's works disuaded them from their attempt.

One divergent line of showman's engines

were the very distinctive ones built by the Savage Brothers of King's Lynn. Some differences from 'standard' are very obvious, including the forked chimney, the heavily inforced and ornamental side sheets and the cutaway roof. This firm were probably the most famous, and certainly the most respected among all builders of 'gallopers', the roundabouts that today are enjoying renewed popularity at steam fairs. Of 8 nhp these compound engines, by 1898, metamorphosed into the ultimate variant, a self-propelled centre engine which towed horses (gallopers) and other machinery of the ride from site to site. But direct mechanical drive proved to be unpopular with showmen and consequently was never developed.

Interestingly, only just over 400 engines were built for showmen, although probably another hundred were converted to their specification. Some which appear in that guise today never saw service on the fairground. Of the 400, Charles Burrells built over half, John Fowler of Leeds 82 and William Foster of Lincoln 68, the balance being shared between eight manufacturers. How the engine was finished, or indeed built, was a matter of long discussion between the would-be owner and the engineering firm – Burrells for example, despite building 207 showmen's engines, claimed that no two were alike.

One line of showman's engines, bought by G.T. Tuby, told of his climb in local politics, and in view of the cost of these machines, his increasing wealth. The first machine, bought to celebrate his election to the Doncaster council, was the 'Councillor'; this was followed by others named 'Alderman' and then 'Mayor'. The last in that line, revealing Tuby's sense of humour, was 'Ex-Mayor'.

Although only 10 nhp, the big showman's engines could easily handle a tail load of 30 tonnes, and, with a top speed of 20 mph (30 kph), a 100 mile (160 km) journey in a day, however long, was possible. But to recapture the flavour of the old fairgrounds it is best to stand next to a dimly lit, warm, Burrell in late evening, listening to her ticking over at 140 rpm and sense the latent power held in check. The majesty of steam indeed.

Rollers roll on

Probably the most evocative steam machinery of all to anyone over the age of 40, road rollers have a unique charm. Prior to general adoption, most roads were rebuilt by broken stone being dumped in the worst potholes and being ground in by the wheels of waggons. Where chalk was the favoured material this rapidly became a white sticky, seemingly bottomless, morass in wet weather, whereas when local flints were used in Birmingham they crippled horses' feet to such an extent that in 1880 the local council purchased a double stone roller, which in the wet seasons required 'ten horses or thirty men from the Poor[house]' to pull it.

Stone was broken by men using hammers with resilient hazel shafts who often found this a useful way to earn wages in between potato picking and the beet crop. There can have been little pleasure in sitting by the roadside in all weathers but at least once the 'piece' was done, a worker's day was done, unlike those feeding the insatiable maw of an engine-driven stone crusher/breaker. Early models of stone crushers were similar to the 'stamps' used in Cornish tin mines, but later reciprocating hammers, hopper-fed, were found to be more reliable–but the racket and grit meant only those desperate for work went near them.

Although steam rollers first appeared over a hundred years ago, few were sold as roads were used mainly for local traffic. Even in the 1940s when the horses stopped in our lanes they could munch the grass in the middle as well as that growing at the verges. Little motor traffic ensured that the old waterbound stone surface was still satisfactory and it was only the tyres of cars, and later lorries, that sucked out the fine grit from the road and necessitated the use of tar as a binding agent. From this came the development of specialized tar sprayers or spreaders, rotating grit hoppers and, of course, varied designs of rollers. Interestingly, the first steam rollers used by the Worcestershire County Council were not delivered until April 1907 when Aveling & Porter supplied three rollers (at £335 each), three watercarts, two sets of pumps (for drawing from wells, streams, etc.) and two living vans. The rollers weighed $12\frac{1}{2}$ tons, but were not initially fitted with the scarifiers, which are necessary to break up road surfaces, an action comparable with sanding old paintwork.

At the same time, Cumberland Council had five rollers, none of which weighed more than 10 tons; Gloucester Council preferred 15-ton models, their engineer stating catagorically 'Lighter ones were useless'. Nottingham split the difference at $12\frac{1}{2}$ tons; and of nine counties all but one recommended Aveling & Porter. When the engineer to the Shropshire County Council was asked if he thought steamrollers better than 'the usual way' he replied 'Undoubtedly. Roads should be made for and not by the traffic.' By 1912 ten tonners were the preferred weight bought by the Worcestershire County Council; eight tonners, still Aveling & Porter, appeared in 1918, by which time steam carts brought the road

stone, steam waggons sprayed the tar and steam rollers consolidated the works. These eight tonners remained in work until at least the early 1950s, when in rural districts it was still the habit of mothers to bring children suffering respiratory problems to smell the tar.

I remember once when at school the teacher allowing us to watch a passing steam roller. That machine was a Clayton & Shuttleworth; I remember the name because we had just learned that the shuttle was an item involved in weaving.

Specialized rollers included special narrow gauge models by Greens of Leeds and Aveling & Porter for rolling between tramlines. Tramway companies were, of course, responsible for maintaining the road surface between the tracks and, normally, 45–60 cm (18–24 in.) either side. For this type of work tandem rollers were used where two 'solid' rolls follow one another in line. When used as a full-sized model the makers tried to avoid the inevitable ridging of the ordinary roller, but the design failed for two reasons. Given the road has the normal camber, a tandem roller will always head for the kerb to the detriment of both kerb and manhole covers and on a wet road it has a surprisingly fast and vicious tendency to turn broadside on. The tri-roller, where three rollers in line were used, in addition to such activities gave an atrociously uncomfortable ride; like all rollers it is, of course, unsprung and the presence of a third roll in the middle finds any unevenness of the surface.

Aveling & Porter also marketed a tandem model with a vertical boiler and water-ballasted rolls, a really spiteful machine, especially on cobbles when it would literally dance. Although not the heaviest machines, Fowlers looked the bulkiest, but if they were the behemoths, then those from Mann's Patent Steam Cart were the pygmies. In effect they took one of their standard carts, replaced the front wheels with wider ones and fitted a full width roll at the rear. Officially of six tons weight they were used for patching the road; sales, however, were poor, and their service life rather short – no more than 20 years!

Initially the slight dimple and ridge left in the road surface at the end of each roll by 'traditional' machines as the flywheel slowed and then reversed, did not matter, but with the increasing use of tarmacadam and hence higher vehicle speeds, these irregularities became apparent. Thus Wallis & Steevens in their last design of 1935 eliminated the flywheel and fitted duplex cylinders to give instant reversing. But later the longevity of rollers betrayed them and I well remember seeing in the 1940s an experimental plastic road surface being extruded from a new-fangled machine and the roller, an elderly Aveling & Porter, casually lifting the extrusion up around its front roll and dumping it in bits further on!

Taking fire to the fire

Steam fire engines had a surprisingly long life; although as there was a curious slowness in adapting them to being self-propelled, many brigades changed directly from steam-fired horse-drawn engines to fully motorized models.

Inevitably, the Romans were the first to initiate a fire watch in Britain, detaching a century of soldiers for this purpose in London. Based on the 'Vigiles' of Rome, they were equipped with ladders, ropes, picks, saws, squirts (like giant 3-man syringes) and buckets. They were nicknamed 'Sparteoli'–literally, tarred bucket men.

Alfred the Great and later William the Conqueror passed laws requiring the damping down of fire at night. From William we have the word 'curfew' from the French 'couvre feu' (cover fire). After William's time it took the Great Fire of London in 1666 to start thoughts of new brigades in the minds of insurance companies. Among the first were the Phoenix (1699) and Sun (1710), although their firemen were only paid £1 a year as volunteers. The first effective wheel pump with hand levers and leather hoses was produced in 1720 and operated by volunteers. The first steam-powered pump came in 1829, and was used during the lifetime of the first true fireman, James Braidwood, the Firemaster of Edinburgh, 1824–1832, and London, 1833–1861, who influenced the insurance companies to create the London Fire Engine Establishment. He standardized uniforms into a sensible grey, inspired and trained his men as one would an army and insisted protective leather helmets be worn.

The design of steam fire engines improved steadily, although Braidwood was killed when at the age of 60 he was superintending efforts to quell the great Tooley Street fire and a wall fell on him. Shand Mason of Blackfriars developed a self-propelled engine around 1878, but Merryweather & Sons 'Fire King' range from 1899 was the best known. Steam was usually kept up in the fire station by means of a gas ring and speeds of 25–30 mph (40–50 kph) were regularly recorded, while the largest of them using a 5 cm (2 in.) jet could project water $62\frac{1}{2}$ m (205 ft). Although production continued until 1919, the convenience of the petrol engine was all too apparent, and steam engines ceased to be developed on a large scale by 1910.

1. Seven miles (11 km) of 122 cm (4 ft) track between Bradford and Shelf was built by Bradford Corporation and then leased to the tramway company for 20 years from September 1884 onwards. The locomotive built by Green was painted Prussian blue with gold and white lining and cream windows. The Astbury trailer was similar in colour, but with red lining – civic pride was upheld despite the dirt of industry.

(*top left*) **2.** Engine No. 2 (*left*), built by Kitson and Car No 4 (*right*), Starbuck, both built in 1885, are seen here just after they had been bought by the Dudley, Sedgley & Wolverhampton Tramways. They served a main line of 5 miles (8 km) which was open from 1886 to 1901. The ornate iron work of the upper deck is rather attractive but did not afford much shelter or comfort. The driver and conductors are not wearing uniform.

(*bottom left*) **3.** The St Helens & District Tramways Company operated on just over the 10 miles (16 km) of tramway from St Helens to Prescot, Denton Green and Haydock Park for almost exactly a decade, 1889–99. The nine engines built by Thomas Green & Son, Leeds, and the ten trailers (Lancaster Railway Carriage & Wagon Co.) remained in service until the end. The Burrell condenser on the roof appears to be made from redundant drain pipes.

(*above*) **4.** Rather oddly touched-up by the photographer, the Kitson engine and car belonging to the Huddersfield Corporation Tramways stands at the junction of Halifax Old Road and Birkby Hall Road, c. 1896. The advertisements cannot have improved the airflow over the condenser on the roof. When built the engine cost £800 and its running costs were about 1.25 per mile.

5. Blackburn Corporation tram, 1900. Between 1887 and 1901 the Blackburn Corporation Tramways Company Limited operated two steam-hauled tramway routes: one from the town to Church and one, as shown here, to the cemetery. The first 15 locomotives came from Thomas Green of Leeds and had condensers of a design patented by Charles Burrell & Sons of Thetford, the road locomotive manufacturer. The one in this photograph, No. 16, was built by Beyer Peacock to William Wilkinson's patent. Although Wilkinson only had a handful of employees, he produced ingenious machines that were light, economical and extremely popular. The final drive was by cogwheels, which although noisy caused little loss of power. Two gear ratios were available, giving good acceleration.

6. The monstrous 100-seater, 44 ft (13.4 m) long trailer of the Wolverton and Stoney Stratford Tramways Company towers over the tram engine built by Green. A true road tramway, 3.2 miles (5 km) long, the main line terminus at Stony Stratford is seen c.1910.

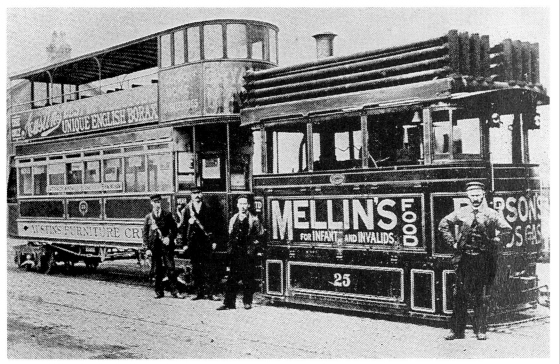

7. A Kitson locomotive No. 25 built in 1897 and Starbuck car No. 18 built in 1886, belonging to the Birmingham and Midland Tramways Ltd, were photographed around the turn of the century. Two conductors or guards were carried at busy times and loads of 100 or more passengers were commonplace. The car was, very unusually, single-ended.

8. A South Staffordshire engine (No. 8) built by Beyer Peacock and designed by Wilkinson. Here, pictured in 1890, it is coupled with a Falcon trailer. The South Staffordshire Tramways Company had two problems to cope with. The first was the narrowness of the streets, which they solved by using a narrow gauge of 3 ft 6 in. (107 cm). The second was their financial difficulties, which, owing to poor management, were never solved. In 1885 they ran over 437,000 miles (700,000 km), carried 3,438,819 passengers and still lost money!

9. Trams in John William Street, Huddersfield, c. 1906. Huddersfield Corporation Tramways was one of the larger operators, having 23½ miles (38 km) of track. The track gauge was designed to allow standard railway waggons to be hauled to and from various works, although this facility was rarely used.

10. A Hughes Patent tramway engine on the Swansea & Mumbles Railway in 1877, during a brief experiment with steam power. After reverting to horse haulage, the railway company later used conventional steam engines on its 5 mile (8 km) length track, albeit in conjunction with long trains of double-deck tramcars.

11. Although a roadside tramway, the Wantage is included as being the nearest British example to the continental '*Kleinbahn*'. The engine was a rarity, being built to James Matthews' patent by Fox Walker of Bristol in 1879. Purchased in 1885, it remained in service until the tramways' closure to passenger traffic on 31 July 1925. The diminutive passenger cars contrast with the Wolverton 100-seater.

12. Claimed at the time to be the 'last steam car in England', this Green-built engine and its trailer is seen at Waterroot, Bacup, on 20 July 1909 when the Rossendale Valleys Tramway Company ceased operating steam transport. The condition of the road surface explains why these trams were so popular.

13. Brand new ex-works Clarkson steam omnibus for use in London.

14. Hancock's Automaton, a 22-seater. Possibly the finest of all his creations, built in 1835.

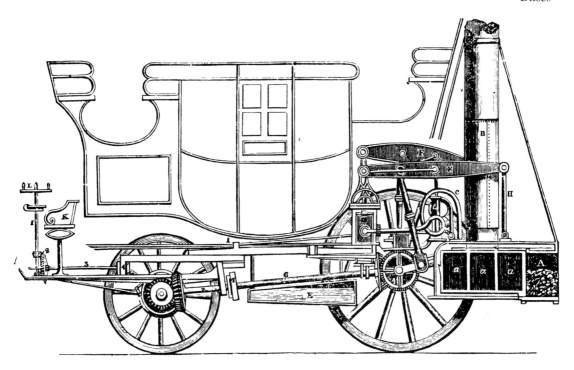

15 Burstall & Hill's coach, built in 1829. (*Above*) A pioneer model with four-wheel-drive by shafts and gears, twin 'motor' (actually cylinders) and balanced steering.

(*Below*) The De Dion Bouton steam tractor of 1898, a linear descendant of the Gurney drags of the 1820s. The machine was designed to haul horse-buses.

(*top left*) **16.** The Straker steam bus. The North Staffordshire Railway called these into service when the planned opening of the Leek & Manifold Light Railway on 17 June 1904 was threatened by the incompletion of the section between Leek and Waterhouses. Two Straker steam buses were purchased and filled the gap from 23 May 1904 to 1 July 1905; later they were converted to pantechnicons.

(*bottom left*) **17.** Apparently a one-off, this Thorneycroft steam bus entered service in London where it was operated by the London Road Car Company between March and May 1902; the body was from a horse bus.

(*above*) **18.** A Lifu steam bus of the Mansfield Motor Car Company Ltd in 1898. This model, *Pioneer*, had a short life, although a similar, or possibly the same, vehicle operated between Torquay and Paignton on 1899.

(*top left*) **19.** A most unusual version of a steam bus was this Sentinel; it was fitted with wooden benches by the Newcastle Corporation and used by armaments workers in around 1918.

(*bottom left*) **20.** One of a number of Darracq-Serpollet operated by the Metropolitan Steam Bus Company during 1907–12.

(*right*) **21.** The chassis design for the 1903 Clarkson steam bus.

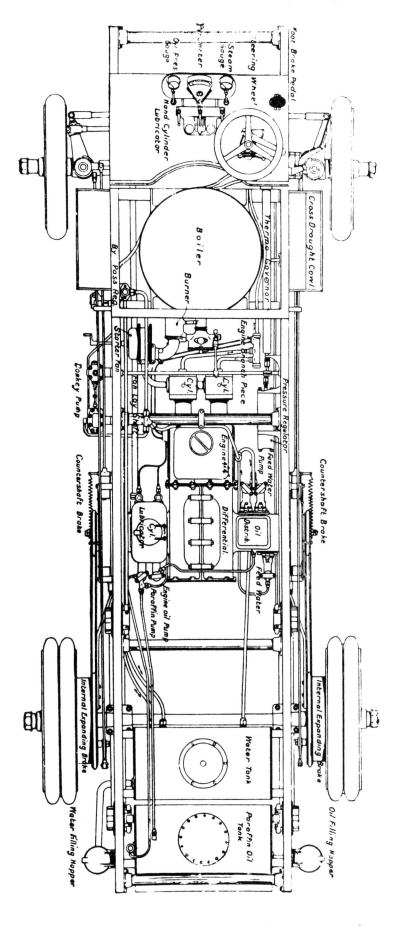

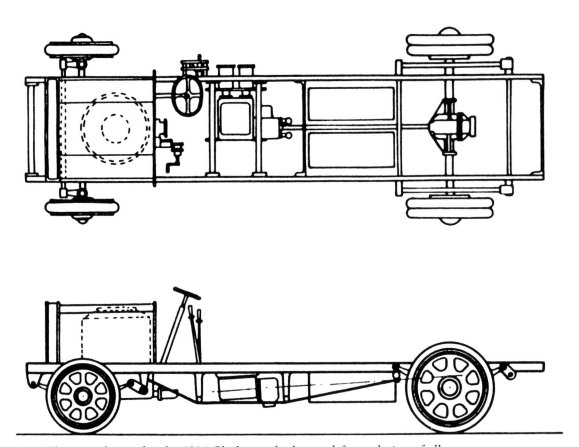

22. The new chassis for the 1914 Clarkson; the last and finest design of all.

23. A 'National' Clarkson steam bus crosses Trafalgar Square in about 1910.

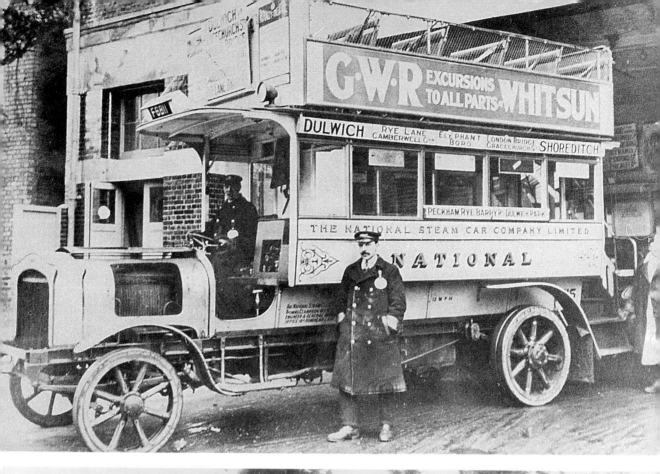

(top left) **24.** A National steam bus, vehicle No. 115, about to leave Nunhead Garage. The service commenced on 8 June 1913 and then transferred to the London General Omnibus Company as route 43/43A on 1 January 1914.

(bottom left) **25.** Another National Clarkson, but unusually this model is a coke-burner, in use in 1917.

(above) **26.** A Clarkson steam bus, 1916. The life of National steam buses may well have been prolonged by the shortage of transport during the First World War. This vehicle was probably used for training clippies. Thomas Clarkson, the designer, is standing behind the rear wheel.

27. A Clarkson steam bus, probably ex-Nantwich & Crewe Motor Bus Company, watering up at Starbeck, Harrogate, c.1911. The weakness of these condensing steam engines was their consumption of copious quantities of water.

(top right) **28.** The bus which was operated between Chagford and Exeter by the London & South Western Railway between June 1905 and May 1908.

(bottom right) **29.** 16-seater Clarkson steam buses in Cheddar Station yard on the Great Western Railway service from Cheddar to Burnham, early 1905. These machines were first based at Bridgnorth and later transferred to Bridgwater.

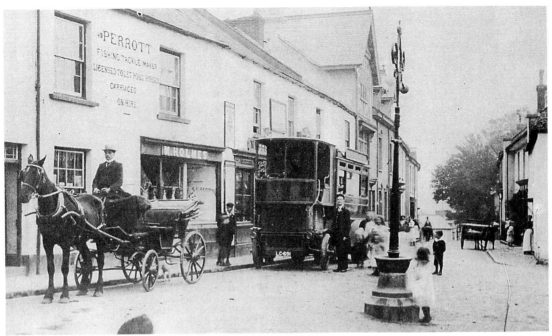

30. *'I say Fellow, give my Buggy a charge of Coke, your Charcoal is so D—d dear.'*

A sketch of 1829 which foretells the lament of today's motorists. The artist, H. Alken, must have closely observed these vehicles as all the components are recognizable.

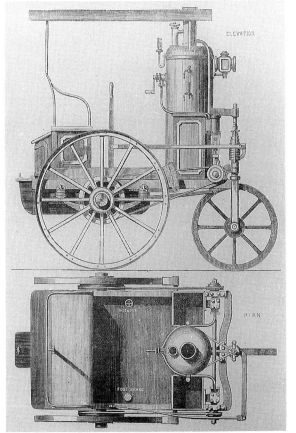

31 and 32. Between 1786 and 1840 around 52 vehicles were built, varying from Hancocks buses to tiny 1- and 2-seaters. After a quiet spell there was a plethora of building in the 1860s ranging from relatively clumsy machines like this (*above*), built by H.P. Holt of Headingley in 1866, to the elegance of L. J. Todd's 'one horse road steamer to carry two persons' (*left*) of 1869.

(*left*) **33 and 34** The Grenville carriage built in 1875 and probably the oldest steam car in usable condition, is seen here both in service and in the Bristol Museum where it now resides. The boiler was by Shand Mason (famed for his fire engines), and the machine has two cylinders and solid teak wheels. The Grenville can reach a top speed of 18 mph (30 kph) but averages 10 mph (16 kph). Water consumption is approximately 4 gallons/mile (11 litres/km), and as the car has to be refilled every 10–12 miles (16–19 km), journeys are somewhat prohibited.

(*above*) **35.** This waggonette, or car, was built by Sidney Soame at Marsham, Norfolk, probably in 1894 (VCC date, 1897). Two gears give a speed of around 15 mph (24 kph), although in wet weather the belt drive suffers from the inevitable problem of slipping. An oddity of the machine is that the stoker at the back also applied the brake which, given his lack of visibility, could have been dangerous. Soame was a particularly ingenious engineer, being credited with developing the first steam-driven roundabout.

THE CRAIGIEVAR EXPRESS 1897

36. The Craigievar Express, homebuilt by a postman Andrew Lawson, in 1895.

37. A 1903 advertisement for steam cars – car-selling one-upmanship in its infancy.

38. The Serpollet standard superheated-steam car with its four-cylinder, high speed engine, and overhead camshaft operating rows of mushroom valves. Leon Serpollet is at the wheel for the Cordingley Show in 1901.

39. This steam motorcycle is thought to be a Halesan, possibly one of a small batch built before the First World War. It is neat and relatively compact, but exposed chains, no mudguards and lack of name makes one wonder whether it was an unfinished prototype.

40 and 41 The famous ex-'Dallifol', now Hilde-brand, built c.1887 and of German origin. Coke is fed from the hopper between the frame members, while the 'mudguard' holds 5 gallons of water. Figure 40 shows the machine more or less as it is now, and figure 41 while being prepared for exhibition in the 1940s.

42 and 43 The Pearson &
Cox represented the finest
steam motorcycle of its era
and its components are
shown here as in December
1922. **42.** (*Above*) The
power unit: double-acting
water pump (F); exhaust
pipe (H); paraffin tank (at
rear of seat); and water tank
(triangular tank on right).
43. (*Right*) The controls:
steam release valve (C);
water control valve lever (D);
paraffin pressure gauge (I);
steam pressure gauge (J).

44. The complexity of a steam motorcycle combination. Containing an old Locomobile engine and boiler, this machine whistled around for at least a decade before 1937. With a mere 30 mph (50 kph) maximum speed and a wicked thirst for petrol, it was withdrawn from the public highway in 1937.

45. A beautiful Brown and May 6 nhp portable, built in 1880.

46. A portable engine being used in Sweden to power a pulverizer to grind peat. The model here is a 1905 Munktells machine and a narrow gauge tipper waggon is used for the ground peat.

47. Farm workers with a 7 nhp portable built by the Wantage Engineering Company in 1907. The machine was supplied to Thomas Saunders of Buckland near Reigate in 1892.

48. Without the ubiquitous water cart neither the humble portable engine in the rickyard nor the magnificent traction on the highway would get far.

49. Built far too late to change history, this 4 nhp Garrett 'Suffolk Punch' was a manufacturers' flop, with only four being completed. In its 1919 form, it would be used by only a steam enthusiast for direct ploughing when tractors were relatively inexpensive. By contrast, the Garrett Compound Steam Tractor, used for road haulage, was one of their best sellers, being both fast and very economical to run.

50. In the original 1 m (3 ft) long engraving there are six of the waggons being hauled by Boydell's 'Traction-Engine and Endless Railway', a total load in excess of 50 tonnes. Built by Charles Burrell of Thetford in 1856, 'Hercules' was very advanced in design terms; after a year or two it was withdrawn, primarily as the wheel plates and their linkages made of cast iron fractured too easily.

51. This timber tractor, photographed around 1918, is a Mann overtype of 1914. The men pictured here may be POWs.

52. A Naylor tractor of 1906, made in Hereford. With a 5-ton capacity, its only speed limit was that imposed by law; the manufacturers claimed that owing to the excellent springing, 10 mph (16 kph) was perfectly feasible even for carrying 'delicate materials'.

53. The UX 9728, serial No. 13784, represents the family of Foden tractors, designed and used as heavy haulers; these more or less equated with the power units of articulated lorries. The model here, photographed in 1968, was built in 1931, with a 6-nhp and 8-ton capacity.

54. The rival to the Foden was the Sentinel 'DG' class. Designed as a timber tractor for use on forested roads they were very successful for their required purpose. Boiler 275 psi, 650 rpm, built 1935 and, like the Foden, photographed in 1968.

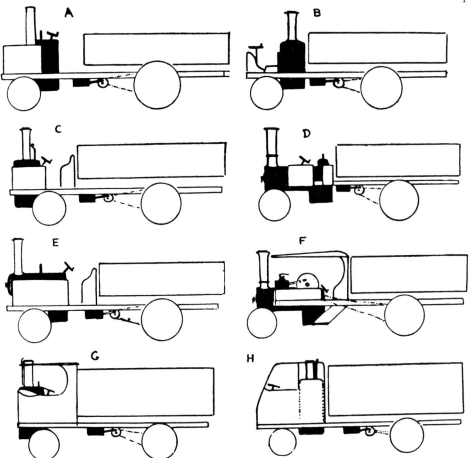

55. Diagram indicating positions of boiler, engine, and driver adopted at various times (first published in *The First Hundred Road Motors*, by R.W. Kinder). There was some parallel development of differing types by the same makers, and the dates given are approximate only.

A—Undertype, boiler behind fron axle, driver rear of boiler: 1898 to 1905, by Londonderry, Stewart and Thornycroft.

B— Undertype, boiler behind front axle, driver in front: 1900 to 1906 by Carters, Coulthard, English, Halley and Hercules.

C—Undertype, boiler in front of axle, driver behind boiler: 1900 to 1910 by Bayley, Garrett, Jesse Ellis, Lifu, Leyland, Robertson, Robey, S.M., St Pancras, Sentinel, Straker, Thames, Wantage.

D—Undertype, loco-type boiler, driver at side: 1899 to 1907 by Bretherton & Bryan and Mann.

E— Undertype, short horizontal boiler, driver behind: 1905 to 1909 by Allchin, Beyer Peacock, Foster, Hindley, Mann, Stewart, Straker, Thornycroft.

F— Overtype, loco-type boiler, driver behind: 1901 to 1927 by Allchin, Aveling & Porter, Burrell, Clayton, Foden, Foster, Garrett, Mann, Ransomes, Robey, Sentinel, Straker, Tasker, Wallis & Steevens.

G—Undertype, continuation of C: 1911 to 1930 by Atkinson, Clayton, Fowler, Garrett, Leyland, Sentinel, and Robey.

H—Undertype, revival of B: 1930 to 1939 by Foden and Sentinel.

56. An advertisement for C & A Musker's steam motor waggons.

57. A Londonderry lorry (named after the Marquis of Londonderry who owned the works). Built by the Seaham Harbour Engine Works, Co. Durham, in 1906, this was used to transport goods from the area around Stanley to Durham. Each had a 5-ton capacity and top speed of 5.5 mph (8.85 kph).

58 and 59 John I. Thornycroft & Co. of Basingstoke manufactured steam lorries between 1896 and 1907. 'Dorothy', No. 39 of 1901, is a 5-tonner rated at 5 nhp.

60. Foden lorries, Kings' Yard, Bishops Lydeard, 1930s.

61. Foden lorries again, Town Ales, Burton-on-Trent, 1920s.

72

62. Robey lorries, Charringtons' Warehouse, London, 1920s.

63. The lorries of the Mann Patent Steam Cart & Wagon Company of Leeds were well known in their day, but this 5-tonner of Samuel Smith, the brewers at Tadcaster, looks rather down-at-heel in 1920.

(*top left*) **64.** John Hughes of North Wales, the proud owner of a Mann steam cart in 1904.

(*bottom left*) **65.** An early Foden 5-tonner, here being used by dustmen; behind it is a tipping waggon.

(*above*) **66.** Steam lorries and trailers in Buckingham Palace Road in 1921. Although the miners were on strike, the vehicles are loading 50 tons of coal for distribution. It is probable that Queen Mary had requested the coal for the poor of London.

67. In the days of the British Empire coal was the most common fuel. Many houses had a coal cellar into which the fuel could be poured via a manhole in the pavement.

68. A Robey steam lorry owned by Charringtons. To compensate for the long boiler, the front axle was set well back, thus reducing the turning circle. Steam-powered lorries were a logical choice for a coal merchant.

76

69. A somewhat bedraggled Foden photographed in the Lake District around 1956 towards the end of its working life. The lid on the chimney shows that even then someone still loved it.

70. Looking thoroughly at home, a Foden 12364 of 1926, once a tar sprayer, chugging-uphill.

71. An unusual modification for a Yorkshire-built Mann steam cart. This tar sprayer was built in the Highways & Local Government Department workshops in Adelaide in 1922, and is seen in 1925.

72. A Bass Foden steam waggon outside a pub belonging to the Salt & Co Brewery, who were taken over by Bass in 1927. The condition of the machine contrasts rather dramatically with that in figure 63.

73. During the First World War vehicles and crops were sequested by the armies fighting on the Western Front. Here, a Foden steam waggon, being used in Britain is carrying hay for army horses.

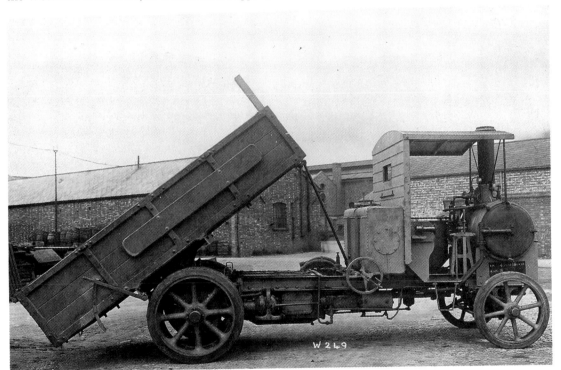

74. A lorry from Peter Brotherhood Ltd of Peterborough, just one of three waggons built in 1920/1. Drive unusually was by side shafts and gears, rather than chain-type of many of their competitors. Schweppes bought one such lorry and commented on the silence and 'wonderful efficiency' of the boiler.

(*above*) **75.** Yorkshire waggons owned by the South African Breweries, Pietermaritzburg, Natal, c.1912. The lack of a cab was less vital in that climate, but heatstroke was a very real hazard.

(*top right*) **76.** A Yorkshire steam waggon built for and supplied to the Great Western Railway in 1905. In company with three trailers, it was used to provide a goods link from Henwick Station as far as Standford-on-Teme Bridge.

(*bottom right*) **77.** The Yorkshire lorry was always famous for its speed; this was not relevant to the gulley emptier here pictured in Pepper Road, Hunslet, near Leeds.

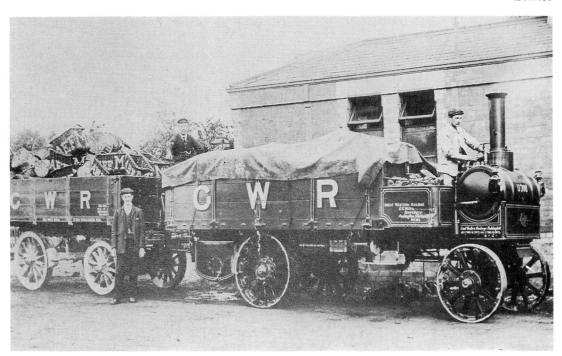

78 and 79 Two views of the same works near the Anchor Inn at Bleadon on the A371 Weston-Super-Mare/Bridgwater road in 1930. The vehicles visible are Yorkshire Sixes, made by the Yorkshire Patent Steam Waggon Co. of Leeds. They differed from most lorries insofar as the boiler was positioned transversely–a feature that made visibility difficult. The vehicles, even in this works unit, were painted dark blue with gold lettering.

80. A Sentinel tar tanker. The ultimate use for a steam lorry was as a tar tanker because the steam-heated coils kept the tar liquid as no petrol vehicle could. Pneumatic tyres represented a considerable improvement in ride.

81. The most versatile of all Sentinels was the tipper. Heavy loads were easily carried—coal, sand and gravel, black ash or shale or even ingots of steel.

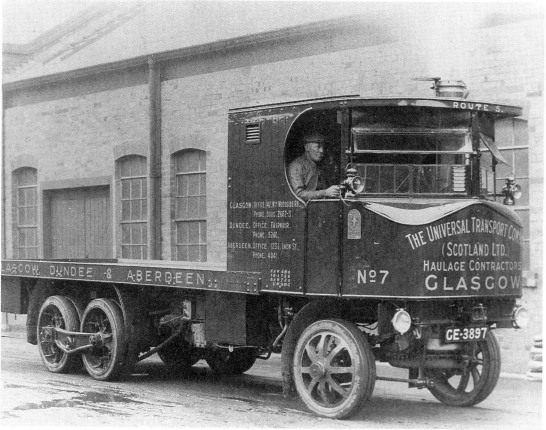

(*top left*) **82.** Perhaps the lorry design that most people associate with the name of Sentinel is the three axle DG6 general purpose body. Chain drive, solid tyres, infinite torque, and, despite a permitted speed of 12 mph (19.3 kph), it could do up to 40 mph (65–70 kph).

(*bottom left*) **83.** A DG6 lorry owned by the Universal Transport Company, fitted with electric headlights. 1920s.

(*above*) **84.** A Sentinel owned by Newman & Masters, Motor Engineers. Particularly noteworthy are the 'Gripfast' tyres, contrasting with the normal smooth solids on the front.

85. Standard Sentinel loaded with Henson's bottled ales and stout.

86. A Super Sentinel, updated with pneumatic tyres, but still in service in Redruth in 1963.

87. One of the last models of Sentinel to be made. The S4, shaft-driven, with a four-cylinder engines of 124 bhp and balanced steam brakes first appeared in 1936. This demonstrator, subsequently registered UJ 5862, is, fortunately, preserved today.

88. An advertisement for a McLaren traction engine.

(*above*) **89.** Two of the Fowlers supplied for transportation purposes during the Anglo-Boer war haul guns over Sir Lowry's Pass 30 miles (50 km) from Cape Town, c.1900.

(*top right*) **90.** A magnificently-restored Swedish engine, distinctly Scandinavian in design. It is a Munktells-type SK6 serial No. 5605, built 1914. With a rating of 10 (30–40 bhp), she is fully sprung, and has chain drive (visible just forward of the rear wheel). The boiler incorporates a steam drier.

(*bottom right*) **91.** Similar in design to the American-built Birdsall engines, this 9 nhp Munktells, built 1908–9, has its components in reverse. The dome is to the rear, and motion, including the gear drive is well forward. Here it is being used to crush the stones on a new road.

92. A Pickford's vehicle in 1941 towing the sort of large load it was familiar with.

93. Coupe Brothers of Sheffield's Fowlers No. 6927 and 8634, together with their Aveling & Porter No. 2952 are seen ready to haul an immense forging from the famous Brightside foundry. The crudity of the waggon contrasts with the sophistication of the engines.

94 and 95 Churches and other buildings were moved by steam vehicles during the Depression when fuel oil was rationed. The picture of the house was taken in Bradshaw, Nebraska in 1944.

96. American engines were required to undertake duties unheard of in Britain. The very size of the country meant that they were supposed to perform as well in the blue grasslands of Kentucky as the black hills of Dakota. Here Chady Atteberry of Blackwell, Oklahoma, demonstrates the hill-climbing ability of a Case machine by driving up a 1 in 2 ramp.

97. A Luton Corporation Aveling & Porter
of 4 nhp tows a tram of 40 bhp—an unusual
vehicular combination.

98. On what is now the A170 Ripon/Scarborough road, a Fowler 9971 (owned by A. Atkinson) prepares to move three loads of furniture.

99. Fir Grove Bridge, Milnrow, is situated roughly 2 km (14 furlongs) up from the Rochdale Branch of the Rochdale Canal. When it was rebuilt in the 1890s, not only did the crowds gather, but two traction engines were used to test the structure for deflection.

100. A Fowler No. 1165 or 1166 of 1868 ran away on a hill leading down from the A607 Lincoln/Grantham road to Navenby (Great Northern) Railway Station c.1900.

(*top right*) **101.** A Marshall No. 61970 complete with modified living van.

(*bottom right*) **102.** This 50 hp 1920 Case engine was owned by Art Kosted of Oklahoma City for years; he often ran it up and down a grassy 45° incline—in the same manner that Case demonstrated their machines to farmers.

103. The general outlines of American engines were very different to the British equivalent. Here (*left to right*) are Case, Minneapolis, Case and Rumely tractions, all having relatively spidery wheels, giving some degree of springing and set-back front axles. Components that British manufacturers tucked away tidily hang outside these machines as though on a Christmas tree.

(*right*) **104.** Possibly the worst work for an engine was stone crushing. This was very hard work and very dusty. Burrell 6 nhp 'Diamond Queen', built in 1897 is seen in the 1950s, working for St Thomas Rural District Council, Exeter, breaking stone to a size suitable for road making.

(*top left*) **105.** A Fowler ploughing engine emitting excessive smoke.

(*bottom left*) **106.** A Burrell on its way home from a rally.

(*above*) **107.** Solid flywheels were often specified by purchasers of traction engines as it was believed that spokes in motion would frighten nervous horses.

108. Showmen used to build up their rides and then power them with a dynamo, until the firm of Savage Brothers from King's Lynn suggested they build the roundabout around the motive power and drive it mechanically. 'Empress' was built in 1898 and decorated with filigree. Instead of a dynamo, a small steam engine was mounted forward of the chimney to power both the organ and the roundabout.

109. 'Enterprise' was much simpler but shows the ironwork required to take the weight of the ride and the linkages. The normal Savage chimney had had to be raised to clear the gearing when in use as a road engine, and the bypass would be used when operating on the fairground. The whole machine looks rather top heavy, and only a few were built.

105

110. Although the mechanism is barely visible above the canopy, this is 'Empress', Savage No. 710 centre engine, when in service with C. Abbott & Sons, Newport Pagnell. Note that no registration plate is carried, the photograph being taken around 1900.

111. E. Morley with his up-to-date ride of 'steam cars' in 1906. The living van on the left is a 'Burton'-type and the engine's chimney is just visible in the centre of the ride.

112. A Burrell engine of 1907, the 'Pride of Worcester'.

113. The first engine bought new by G.T. Tuby & Sons of Doncaster and named to commemorate his appointment to the local council. Painted a light blue with yellow wheels, she was built by Burrells in 1900. This inspired when in use as a road engine, and the bypass would be used when operating on the fairground. The whole machine was rather top heavy, and only a few were built.

114. Before the days when the length and number of towed vehicles was restricted, G.T. Tuby's Burrell 2793, 'The Leader', is seen at Retford, Nottinghamshire, on 5 October 1910.

115. 'Roy Roy' was a product of Garretts of Leiston; there are far fewer preserved Garretts than Burrells nowadays.

116. Burrell 2879 of 1907, 'Princess Royal', a delightful example of a restored showman's engine, with an exquisite miniature engine on her tank. This depicts Pat Collin's Foster engine of 1921, 'The Leader', itself preserved, after remaining in service until 1963.

117. Built to the order of Fred Gray from Hampstead, the Allchin 8 bhp single cylinder engine No. 1246 was registered in May 1903. Pictured here with her load, Fred used her to power his electric galloping horses roundabout. The photograph was taken in Markyate, Hertfordshire, 1904

118. When it was necessary to descend or ascend a hill even on a showman's engine, it was necessary to change gear. This required stopping, 'scotching' or hand-braking the load and manually adjusting the gear wheels. Occasionally, as here at Wooler Bridge, Northumberland, matters still went wrong and the load forced the engine off course.

119. Near Allonby on what is now the B5300, Maryport-Silloth road, A & P Caris's Aveling & Porter engine 'Samson' broke through the decking of the bridge. Luckily the living van (part of a load of five vehicles) remained upright.

(left) **120.** An Aveling & Porter No. 8036 rolls over 1300 counterfeited Cartier 'Santos' watches. M. Alain Perrin, the Managing Director of the firm, decided to show his contempt for the quality of the imitations by squashing them under a steam roller on Park Lane, 1982. 'A bas les inférieures!'

(top) **121.** Roadmaking before the era of the automobile on the A5 near Betws-y-coed 1904. The roller has unusually wide rear rolls and looks far more squat than later designs. This is a Fowler 10-tonner, c.1890.

(bottom) **122.** The Bomford & Eversheds steam roller yard, Salford Priors, Worcestershire in the 1950s. Often models were completely rebuilt here, and some really exceptional feats of engineering took place. The massive piece of ironwork at the rear of the nearest machine is the scarifier, used to rip up the existing surface of a road.

123. The Wallis & Steevens 'Simplicity' roller had all the right factors to be successful, but only fifteen were made, six of which were exported. However, they were long-lived for of the nine home sales, six still survive. The angled boiler was an attempt to overcome the problems of rolling on a gradient. Model 7832, shown here in the Exeter area c.1930, was the prototype and first registered 13 January, 1926.

124. Timeless and typically British. A Ruston & Hornsby roller, 'Success', rests quietly on the verdant roadside.

125. Seemingly a British scene as the men lay bituminous concrete, assisted by a Fowler compound roller in 1924, but behind them are gum trees and the location, the Adelaide to Yorke Peninsula Main Road in South Australia.

126. Aveling & Porter, as befitted their reputation as the most innovative of steam roller manufacturers, made many attempts to lower their machines' centre of gravity and ease the 'ripple' effect left on the tar when the machine reversed. This Australian wood burner, seen in Adelaide 1958, has both a vertical boiler and tandem rollers.

127. Detail of boiler.

(*top left*) **128.** Neat, tidy, and with excellent paintwork, this Aveling-Barford 6-tonner of 4 nhp is an exemplary steam road vehicle.

(*bottom left*) **129.** A Burrell roller No. 3047 'Monarch', rests beside a 'coffin-nosed' Stanley steamer.

(*above*) **130.** A living van, Dorchester c.1920. The living van was a necessary adjunct to the roller and often the traction engine too. This could be used as accommodation during inclement weather or for the men to sleep in when a distance from home. Stuffy in summer and musty in winter, it also housed a variety of insects in the woodwork. Much plainer than a gypsies' van, nonetheless, the living van could be quite homely.

119

(*top left*) **131.** One of the oldest photographs depicting steam fire engines and manual pumps in front of Edinburgh Castle, c.1890.

(*bottom left*) **132.** A steam fire engine in Lauriston, *c.* 1885. When Braidwood was appointed Master of the Fire Engines commanding the Edinburgh Fire Engine Establishment, he introduced Draconian discipline; the firemen were allowed out of the station (other than for calls) for only four hours a week (and only then if no-one else was on leave or sick). Wherever possible he employed sailors, who were used to cramped conditions, poor food, rigid discipline and close confinement.

(*above*) **133.** An engine of unknown origin, but probably a rebuilt Shand Mason of 1882. The passengers look more like dignitaries than firemen, however.

(*top left*) **134.** The Edinburgh Fire Establishment at St Giles in 1873. They are wearing dress uniform with serge jackets and duck trousers.

(*bottom left*) **135.** A horse-drawn steam pump belonging to the Birmingham Fire Office around the turn of the century. The fireman in the brass helmet has a contemporary air compared with his colleagues. The badge on the sleeve of the man on the left is, in fact, a Sun Insurance fire plate; such a badge was normally attached to a house so that the company knew it was insured.

(*above*) **136.** Merryweather Fire King at Angle Park Fire Station, 1908. The brass helmets shown here were introduced in the 1870s, and remained so until the 1930s when the widespread use of electricity with the risk of electrocution from falling overhead wires, made them too hazardous.

137. A spick and span Merryweather Fire King stands ready for action. The Edinburgh Brigade, unlike some, did not keep the boiler simmering by a gas lance, but lit up and went as soon as possible. Photographed at Lauriston, the degree of polish reflects the men's pride in their machine.

138. Possibly the oddest use ever for a York-shire waggon, as a railway 'locomotive'. The objective of the conversion by South African Railways was to haul coaches of farm produce on a 12 mile (19 km) 60 mm (2 ft) gauge spur line on the North Transvaal. The driving wheels ran on the ground outside the rails, but for all its ingenuity the locolorry was withdrawn after a year's service on the iron road in 1924.

139. The locomotive, Billy, built by Andrew Barclay of Kilmarnock (works No. 1881) in 1925, but seen here crossing Level Street, Brierley Hill, on 2 May 1959. The load is being trundled between two parts of Round Oak Ironworks.

Photographic acknowledgements

Elton Collection, Ironbridge Gorge Museum Trust: frontispiece, 14, 30, 50, 109. Wood Visual Communications: 1. R.W. Kidner: 9, 11, 32, 52, 55, 64, 65, 82, 86, 92, 97. Frank D. Simpson: 15b, 17, 18, 19, 20, 24, 26, 27, 29. Ronald H. Clark: 21. Calton Phoenix Collection: 25. City of Bristol Museum & Art Gallery: 33, 34. Kevin Lane Collection: 35, 70, 80, 116. Emap National Publications Ltd: 36, 39–44. The Worthington Williams Collection: 38. The late Douglas Lawson: 45, 48, 49, 104. Rubens Maskinhistoriska Samlingar: 46, 90, 91. Museum of English Rural Life: 47. MB Transport Photographs: 51, 59, 84, 101, 105, 124, 128, 129. Peter Shoesmith: 53, 54, 58, 69, 106, 107, 115, 122, 139. E.G. Pike: 60, 79, 81. Charringtons Solid Fuel: 61, 66–68. Bass Museum: 62, 72, 83, 85. Les Emmott: 63. The Highways Department, South Australia: 71, 125. The Leeds & District Traction Engine Club: 73, 77, 93, 98, 108, 110, 114, 117, 118, 119. Peter Brotherhood Ltd: 74. City of Johannesburg, Africana Museum: 75, 89, 138. British Rail: 76. Woodspring Museum, Weston-super-Mare: 78. Motor Transport: 87. Menno L. Kliewer: 95. Lawrence R. Gibbs: 96, 102, 103. Rochdale Public Libraries: 99. Harold Bonnett: 100. Cartier Ltd: 120. James Gilbey: 123. John Norris: 126, 127. The Braidwood & Rushbrook Museum: 131, 132, 134, 136, 137. The Fire Protection Association: 135.